A STUDY
OF THE FALSE DOCTRINE OF
PREMILLENNIALISM

A Study by Jeff Archer

ONESTONE
BIBLICAL RESOURCES

Published by:
One Stone Press
979 Lovers Lane
Bowling Green, KY 42103

Printed in the United States of America

ISBN 10: 1-941422-04-7
ISBN 13: 978-941422-04-5

Supplemental Materials Available:

➢ Answer Key

➢ Downloadable PDF

www.onestone.com

ONE STONE
BIBLICAL RESOURCES

CONTENTS

INTRODUCTION

As of 2007, the 16 books in the *Left Behind* series authored by Tim Lahaye and Jerry Jenkins had sold 65 million copies. Not only has the series been adapted into three action thriller films, the series has inspired two PC games. This series is one example of the hugely popular doctrine of "premillennialism."

Jehovah's Witnesses, Seventh Day Adventists, Baptists, Worldwide Church of God, Mormons and others teach premillennialism as part of their doctrine.

Study Bibles such as Scofield Study Bible, Ryrie Study Bible and many others teach premillennialism within their notes.

Definitions

1. **Postmillennialism**. "Post" = after, "millennial" = 1,000 years, "ism" = belief. Postmillennialists believe Jesus will return to the earth after His 1,000 year reign. More and more people will be converted until Jesus establishes His kingdom on the earth. This utopia will last for 1,000 years and will end with the coming of Jesus. Some of the "social gospel" efforts to correct society's ills and bring about peace on earth contains postmillennial views.

2. **Amillennialism**. "A" = not, "millennial" = 1,000 years, "ism" = belief. Amellinnialists believe the millennial reign of Jesus is not literal but spiritual. Jesus is reigning from Heaven now over his kingdom/church. This reign will not last for a literal 1,000 years but from Pentecost until the Judgment Day.

3. **Premillenialism**. "pre" = before, "millennial" = 1,000 years, "ism" = a belief. Premillennialists believe the coming of Jesus will be before the 1,000 year reign. Jesus is not now reigning over His kingdom. At some point in the future, (Premillenialists I have read from or spoken to believe the return of Jesus is imminent) Jesus will physically return and sit on a physical throne in Jerusalem and reign for a literal 1,000 years.

Premillennial View

Dispensational Premillennialism

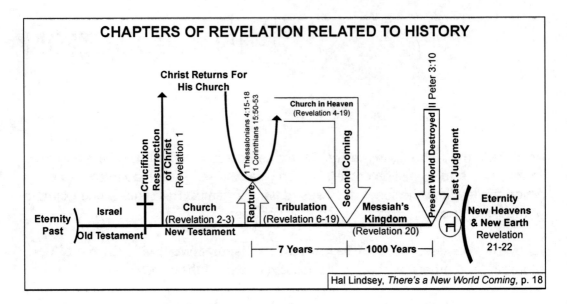

CHAPTERS OF REVELATION RELATED TO HISTORY

Hal Lindsey, *There's a New World Coming*, p. 18

Although there are many types of premillennial doctrines, this study focuses on "dispensational" premillennialism. This doctrine divides history of the world into seven periods or dispensations. The last period will be the millennial reign. Several features of this doctrine are:

1. The promises made to Abraham have never been fulfilled.

2. The kingdom prophesied in the Old Testament is literal/physical rather than spiritual and has not yet been established.

3. Jesus came to the earth the first time to establish His kingdom and to fulfill the promises to Abraham, but was rejected by the Jews.

4. Jesus withdrew His offer to establish His kingdom until He returns to the earth again.

5. To fill the gap in God's plan, Jesus established His Church.

6. Before Jesus returns to the earth a second time, the Jews will re-occupy the land of Promise, the Jewish nation will be re-established, and all Jews will be converted.

7. Jesus will return but only in the air. The saints/Church will be "raptured" up into the clouds to be with the Lord in Heaven.

8. A period of great tribulation will take place on the earth for seven years.

9. At the end of this seven years, the battle of Armageddon will occur and Jesus will return to the earth with all the saints to be victorious. All sinners will be killed.

10. The 1,000 year reign of Jesus will begin ushering in a time of prosperity and utopia. The saints will not die during this period.

11. At the end of the 1,000 year reign, Satan will rally his forces of rebellious saints in the battle of Gog and Magog. Jesus will win this battle.

12. The resurrection of the wicked, destruction of the earth, and the final Judgment will occur.

13. The saints will go to Heaven - a recreated earth and heaven. The sinners will go to Hell.

What examples have you seen of the premillennial doctrine? _____
_____
_____

Biblical View

What problems do you see with the premillennial doctrine? _____
_____
_____
_____

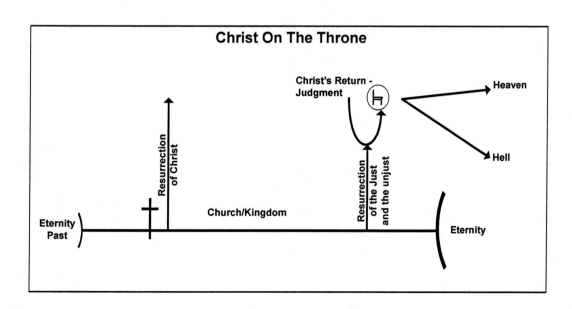

LITERAL OR SPIRITUAL INTERPRETATION?

Premillennial Position

Premillennialists insist on a literal interpretation of prophecy rather than spiritual. For example, God promised David that he would have a descendant who would, "build a house for My name, and I will establish the throne of his kingdom forever," (2 Sam. 7:13). The Premillennialist interprets this promise literally. Jesus is to build a literal/physical house and sit on the literal/physical throne of David in Jerusalem.

"And because hundreds of specific prophecies have already been literally fulfilled—most of them in relation to the first coming of Christ—we know that all the prophecies about the future will be fulfilled literally in the end times, and Christ's return will be fulfilled literally as well," (Tim LaHaye, Charting the End Times, p.11).

"Many teachers today are confusing Christians by teaching that Scripture was never intended to be interpreted literally. Instead, they call for a spiritualizing or allegorizing of the Bible's prophecies. This only leads to confusion!" (LaHaye, p.13)

"Premillennialists believe that theirs is the historic faith of the Church. Holding to a literal interpretation of the Scriptures, they believe that the promises made to Abraham and David are unconditional and have had or will have a literal fulfillment. In no sense have these promises made to Israel been abrogated or fulfilled by the Church, which is a distinct body in this age having promises and a destiny different from Israel's." (Charles Ryrie, The Basis of the Premillennial Faith, p.12)

"The system of spiritualizing Scripture is a tacit denial of the doctrine of verbal, plenary inspiration of the Scriptures which this author holds." (Ryrie, p.35)

Biblical Position - How does God want us to interpret prophecy?

We will talk about more prophecies in lessons to come. These two are given as illustrations.

1. What did God promise to David (2 Sam.7:12-13)? _____

_____

  A. Did Jesus see His kingdom as literal or spiritual (John 18:36)? _____

  _____

  B. How did Peter, by the inspiration of the Holy Spirit, see the fulfillment (Acts 2:30-36)? _____

  _____

2. How did Jesus fulfill the prophecy of Isaiah 61:1-2 (Luke 4:17-21)? _____

_____

Biblical Position

Old Testament Type   **New Testament Antitype**
Was Literal   **Is Spiritual**

God's system of dealing with man went from an emphasis on the literal to an emphasis on the spiritual. Record the difference in the Old Testament type and the New Testament antitype in the following passages.

3. Covenant.

  A. OT type (Exo .34:1) _____

  B. NT antitype (Heb. 8:8-12) _____

4. Place of Worship.

  A. OT type (Jno. 4:21) _____

  B. NT antitype (Jno. 4:23-24) _____

5. Tabernacle.

  A. OT type (Heb. 9:1-10) _____

  B. NT antitype (Heb. 9:11) _____

6. Priesthood.

  A. OT type (Exo. 29:44) _____

  B. NT antitype (1 Pet. 2:9) _____

7. Circumcision.

    A. OT type (Gen. 17:9-13) _____

    B. NT antitype (Col. 2:11) _____

Premillennial Position - God's Ultimate Purpose is Physical

According to Premillennialism, the "unifying principle of the Bible is the GLORY of God and this is worked out in several ways—the program of redemption, the program for Israel, the punishment of the wicked, the plan for the angels, AND THE GLORY OF GOD REVEALED THROUGH NATURE." (Charles Ryrie, Dispensationalism Today, p.44)

Notice the Premillennialist believes God's purpose, among other things, is "the program for Israel" and they understand this as something separate and still in the future from "the program of redemption." The Premillennialist believes Jesus has provided redemption now, but only until Israel is exalted as the world empire in the millennial reign. In this reign, the blessings of the Messianic kingdom will be realized literally/physically. He believes greater blessings will be given to the Jews during this millennial reign than we have right now in Christ.

Biblical Position - God's Ultimate Purpose is Spiritual

8. What are found in Christ right now (Eph. 1:3)? _____
_____

9. How much of the plan of God was gathered together in Christ (Eph. 1:9-10)? _____
_____

10. Is it possible for literal/physical blessings of a millennial kingdom to be greater than the spiritual blessings we have in Christ right now? _____ Explain your answer. _____
_____

PROMISES TO ABRAHAM

Premillennial Position

The Premillennialist would answer "yes" to the following questions, "(1) Does the Abrahamic covenant promise Israel a permanent existence as a nation? If it does, then the Church is not fulfilling Israel's promises, but rather Israel as a nation has a future yet in prospect; and (2) does the Abrahamic covenant promise Israel permanent possession of the promised land? If it does, then Israel must yet come into possession of that land, for she has never fully possessed it in her history" (Charles Ryrie, The Basis of the Premillennial Faith, p.49).

"The unconditional character of the Abrahamic covenant is the crucial issue in making the Abrahamic covenant a basis for premillennialism. If the covenant is unconditional, then the national aspect of it must yet be fulfilled, and premillennialism is the only system of interpretation which makes a place for a national future for Israel in which she possesses her land" (Ryrie, p.53).

"Since the Church does not fulfill the promises of the Abrahamic covenant, Israel herself must fulfill them at a future date. Since only premillennialism has a place for the future fulfillment, it must be the correct system of interpretation" (Ryrie, p.70).

"The church is unique in the plan of God and separate from His plan for Israel. While the church partakes of the spiritual promises of the Abrahamic Covenant as fulfilled through Christ, Israel, and not the church, will fulfill her national destiny as a separate entity after the Rapture and Tribulation and during the Millennium" (Tim LaHaye, Charting the End Times, p.48).

Biblical Position - Promises to Abraham

1. Summarize the promises God made to Abraham and his descendents (Gen. 12:1-3).

A. _____

B. _____

C. _____

Biblical Position - Land Promise

2. What was the extent of the land promise (Gen. 15:18-21)? _____
_____

3. Was God going to give Abraham's descendents this land? Was it conditional (Gen. 15:13-17)? _____
_____

4. Did God fulfill the land aspect of the promise to Abraham by giving Israel all the land (Joshua 21:43-45)? _____
_____

5. Did Israel possess all of the promised land (1 Kings 4:20-21)? _____
_____

6. After it was given, was the retention of the land conditional? If so, on what conditions (Deut. 28)? _____
_____
_____

Biblical Position - Nation Promise

7. Did God fulfill the national aspect of the promise to Abraham by the children of Israel becoming a nation (Exo. 19:5-8)? _____
_____

8. After the children of Israel became a nation, was their continual existence conditional (Deut. 28; 30:19-20)? _____
_____

Biblical Position - Seed Promise

9. What type of blessing did God have in mind when He made the Seed promise (Gal. 3:8)? _____

10. Was this promise only for physical Israel (Gal. 3:14)? _____
_____

11. Who was the "Seed" (Gal. 3:16)? _____

12. Has the seed aspect of the promise to Abraham been fulfilled (Gal. 3:29)? _____
_____

13. Is the reception of this blessing through Christ, the Seed, conditional (Gal. 3:26-
27)? _____

14. If the promises made to Abraham have been fulfilled, what effect does that have
on the doctrine of Premillennialism? _____
_____

RESTORATION OF ISRAEL

Premillennial Position

"All the facts discussed previously, to the point that Israel continues as a nation forever, possesses the land forever, is not disinherited, is not supplanted by the church, and that Israel's basic covenants are dependent upon God's faithfulness alone for fulfillment, combine to require Israel's restoration after these centuries of dispersion and chastening. The conclusion that Israel has a future restoration is based upon these facts along with the voluminous testimony of the prophets concerning Israel's coming golden age," (Walvood, The Millennial Kingdom, p. 184).

"Some time in the future there will be a seven-year period climaxed by the visible return of Jesus Christ. ...The one event which many Bible students in the past overlooked was this paramount prophetic sign: Israel had to be a nation again in the land of its forefathers. Israel a nation—a dream for so many years, made a reality on 14 May 1948 when David Ben-Gurion read the Declaration of Independence announcing the establishment of a Jewish nation to be know as the State of Israel. ...The same prophets who predicted the world-wide exile and persecution of the Jew also predicted their restoration as a nation. ...This restoration was to come about in the general time of the climactic seven-year countdown and its finale—the personal appearance of the Messiah to deliver the new state from destruction. Right here a careful distinction must be made between 'the physical restoration' to the land of Palestine as a nation, which clearly occurs shortly before the Messiah's coming and the 'spiritual restoration' of all Jews who have believed in the Messiah just after His return to this earth. ...'Truly I say to you, this generation will not pass away until all these things take place." (Matt.24:34) What generation? Obviously, in context, the generation that would see the signs—chief among them the rebirth of Israel. A generation in the Bible is something like forty years. If this is a correct deduction, then within forty years or so of 1948, all these things could take place. Many scholars who have studied Bible prophecy all their lives believe that this is so," (Hal Lindsey, The Late Great Planet Earth, pp. 42-54). Hal Lindsey wrote this book in 1970.

Biblical Position - Physical Remnant

1. Before Israel entered the Promised Land, Moses told the people how they would be cursed if they did not follow the Law of God.

   A. What consequences would they suffer (Deut. 28:49-53)? _____
   _____

   B. What consequences would they suffer (Deut. 28:64-68)? _____
   _____

   C. These curses became fulfilled prophecies when the Assyrians captured Israel in 722 BC (2 Kings 17) and the Babylonians captured Judah in 605, 597 and 586 BC (2 Kings 24-25).

   D. What was the condition for their return (Deut. 30:1-8)? _____
   _____

2. About 730 BC, what did Isaiah say would happen in this restoration (Isa. 10:20-23)? __
   _____

3. Who would be the servant of God to bring this restoration about (Isa. 44:26-45:4)? __
   _____

4. When did Jeremiah say the restoration would occur (Jer. 25:11; 29:10-14)? _____
   _____

5. When did God say these restoration prophecies were fulfilled (Ezra 1:1-4)? _____
   _____

   A. Zerubbabel returned 536 BC, Ezra 458 BC and Nehemiah 444 BC.

6. What promise of Moses (in Deut. 30) did God through Nehemiah say was fulfilled by the remnant's return to Judah (Neh. 1:8-11)? _____
   _____

Biblical Position - Spiritual Remnant

7. What did Isaiah prophecy would happen a second time (Isa. 11:11)? _____
   _____
   _____

8. Who would lead this restoration (Isa. 11:1-2, 10)? _____
   _____

9. When was this fulfilled (Acts 2)? _____

_____

10. Paul quoted Isaiah 11:10 in Romans 15:12 to show the Gentiles were always to be a part of the blessings of God. If the promise of restoration is only for the Jews, as the Premillinnialist says, where does this leave the Gentiles (Rom. 15:8-13)? _____

_____

_____

11. Paul talks about the (spiritual) "remnant" in Romans 11:5 to help the Gentile Christians understand they are part of God's plan for blessings as well as the Jews. In Romans 11:16-24, he used the figure of an olive tree to show the relationship of the Jew and Gentile in God's new plan.

   A. Who are the branches broken off (Rom. 11:17)? _____

   _____

   B. Who are the grafted in branches (Rom. 11:17)? _____

   _____

   C. About what did the grafted in branches need to be careful (Rom. 11:18-21)? __

   _____

   D. What will happen to the natural branches having been cut off if they repent (Rom. 11:23-24)? _____

   _____

   _____

12. If there are no more prophecies for physical restoration to be fulfilled by physical Israel, what does this do to the teaching of premillennialism? _____

_____

KINGDOM PROPHECIES AND REJECTION OF JESUS

Premillennial Position

"It has been shown in tracing the theme of the Gospel of Matthew that the pivotal point in the Lord's ministry to Israel was reached in the twelfth chapter, where the rejection of Israel by Christ, because of their announced rejection of Him, and the withdrawal of the offer of the kingdom is recorded. Gaebelein, speaking of the events in chapters eleven and twelve, says: 'It is the great turning point in this Gospel and with it the offer of our Lord to Israel as their King, as well as the offer of the kingdom ceases!'" (Pentecost, Things to Come, p. 463).

"This is a crucial point in the interpretation of the Davidic covenant. The kingdom of heaven (literally of the heavens, not in the heavens) which Christ faithfully offered while on the earth was the very same earthly, Messianic, Davidic kingdom which the Jews expected from the Old Testament prophecies. But it is a matter of history that such a kingdom was not ushered in at the first advent of Christ. Does this abrogate the covenant, or was something new introduced at that time? In the understanding of the mystery form of the kingdom lies the answer. Two things enter into this: the rejection of the offered kingdom, and the Lord's actual teaching concerning the mystery form of the kingdom." (Ryrie, The Basis of the Premillennial Faith, p.93-95)
"Evidence of the rejection of the kingdom is found in many places. ... (It is significant that at the end of this chapter [Matt.11], in which occurs this first evidence of the rejection of the kingdom, these words appear: "Come unto me, all ye that labour and are heavy laden, and I will give you rest" (verse 28), for these are words which are entirely foreign to the kingdom message.) ...In Matthew 13 the Lord is introducing the mysteries of the kingdom, that is, something that was formerly unknown but which is now revealed. The kingdom itself was not unknown to the Old Testament prophets as has been shown, but the mystery form of the kingdom was unknown then and could not be known until Christ's genuine offer of the kingdom had been rejected. It is the mystery form of the kingdom of which the Lord speaks in this chapter, and this is the form in which the kingdom is established in this present age," (Ryrie, The Basis of the Premillennial Faith, p.93-95).

Biblical Position - The Rejection of the Jews

1. Was the rejection by the Jews a surprise to God? Did Isaiah say the Jews would accept or reject Jesus (Isa. 53:1-4)? _____

_____

Note: John 12:37-38 - During the week leading up to the death of Christ (well after Matt. 12), John said the Jews fulfilled this prophecy by rejecting Jesus.

2. What did the Psalmist prophesy would happen to the Messiah (Psalms 118:22-24)?

_____

3. Did the rejection of Jesus force Him to change His plans (Lke. 24:46-47)? _____

_____

4. Did the Jews reject Jesus (Matt. 11:21-24)? _____

_____

5. The Premillennialist says because of this rejection Jesus withdrew His offer to establish the earthly kingdom and changed to the "mystery of the kingdom." Please read through the end of Matthew 11 and the beginning of chapter 12. Do you see the change? _____

_____

_____

6. After this supposed change, Matthew 14:13-21 records the miracle of the feeding of the 5,000. John records the same miracle in John 6:1-13. Please read John 6:14-15. What did the Jews want to do with Jesus? _____

_____

A. Was Jesus pleased that the Jews wanted to make Him their king (Jno. 6:15)? __

_____

B. Why not (Jno. 6:26-27, 61-66)? _____

_____

_____

Biblical Position - The Kingdom was "at hand"

7. When did John say the promised kingdom was coming (Matt. 3:2)? _____

_____

8. When did Jesus say the promised kingdom was coming (Mrk. 1:14-15)? _____

_____

9. When was the kingdom to come with power (Mrk. 9:1)? _____
_____

Note: This promise/prophecy of Jesus was made 6 days before the transfiguration (Mrk. 9:2). The parallel account in Matthew's Gospel is in chapter 17, which is AFTER the supposed withdrawal of the offer to establish His kingdom in Matthew 12.

A. When was this fulfilled (Acts 1:8, 2:1-4)? _____
_____

Biblical Position - Kingdom of Heaven

10. Did Jesus change the nature of the kingdom He offered from physical to "mystery form?" _____

A. Before Matthew 12, what kind of birth was necessary to enter the kingdom (Jno. 3:5)? _____

B. After Matthw 12, where was the kingdom going to rule (Lke. 17:20-21)? _____
_____

C. After Matthew 12, what is the nature of the kingdom (Jno. 18:36)? _____
_____

D. After Matt. 12, why did Jesus come into the world (Jno. 18:37)? _____
_____

11. Suppose the premillennial doctrine is true—

1) Jesus intended to establish an earthly kingdom during His first coming to the earth.

2) He was not able to establish this earthly kingdom because the Jews rejected Him.

Then:

A. Does this qualify as a failure on Jesus' part? _____
_____

B. Will Jesus be able to accomplish His goal of establishing an earthly kingdom at His second coming to the earth? What if the Jews reject Him again? _____
_____
_____

KINGDOM / CHURCH ESTABLISHED AND JESUS IS ON HIS THRONE

Premillennial Position

"The main point in question is whether or not the Church is a distinct body in this present age. If the Church is not a subject of Old Testament prophecy, then the Church is not fulfilling Israel's promises, but instead Israel herself must fulfill them and that in the future. In brief, premillennialism with a dispensational view recognizes the Church as a distinct entity, distinct from Israel in her beginning, in her relation to this age, and in her promises. ...The first question asked above is answered by the teaching of the Scriptures that the Church is an intercalation. It makes little difference to the doctrine whether one wishes to call the Church a parenthesis or an intercalation, but since a parenthesis is related primarily to grammar and an intercalation does mean an introduction of a period of time into a calendar, the latter word seems more ac-curate. ...The chief point of difference with the amillennialist concerns whether or not the truth of a mystery was completely hidden in the Old Testament. ...The Church is a mystery in the sense that it was completely unrevealed in the Old Testament and now revealed in the New Testament. ...Since this is so, the Church is not fulfilling Israel's promises, but she will be taken out of the way before God again deals with Israel," (Ryrie, The Basis for the Premillennial Faith, p. 126-138).

"This whole mystery program was not revealed until after the rejection of Christ by Israel. It was after the rejection of Matthew 12:23-24 that the Lord first makes a prophecy of the coming church in Matthew 16:18. It is after the rejection of the Cross that the church had its inception in Acts 2. It was after the final rejection by Israel that God called out Paul to be the Apostle of the Gentiles through whom this mystery of the nature of the church is revealed. The church is manifestly an interruption of God's program for Israel, which was not brought into being until Israel's rejection of the offer of the Kingdom," (Pentecost, Things to Come, p. 201).

"In the parables (Matt.13:1-50) the Lord outlines the programs for the development of the theocratic kingdom during the period of the King's absence, and announces the inception of an entirely new, unheralded, and unexpected program—the church. ...Thus we see the Lord is preparing the disciples for the withdrawal of the offer of the kingdom and the institution of a new program and age before the kingdom program is consummated," (Pentecost, p. 463-464).

"The New Testament teaches that the church was an unrevealed mystery in the Old Testament (Romans 16:25-26; Ephesians 3:2-10; Colossians 1:25-27), which is why she began suddenly, without warning, in Acts 2, and why this age will end suddenly and mysteriously, without warning, at the Rapture. Therefore, the church has no earthly prophetic destiny beyond the Rapture." (Tim LaHaye, Charting the End Times, p.48) "Finally, the New Testament nowhere identifies the present work of Christ with the throne and the kingdom of David, but rather specifically separates the periods of present Gentile blessing from that of Israel's future glory," (Ryrie, The Basis for the Premillennial Faith, p. 104).

Biblical Position - Kingdom Prophecies

1. What promise was made to David (2 Sam. 7:12-13)? _____
_____

2. How would the descendents of David know God remembered His promise (Isa. 7:13-14)? _____
_____

3. When would the kingdom be established (Dan. 2:44-45)? _____
_____

Biblical Position - Jesus' Fulfillment

4. Who gave birth to Jesus (Lke. 1:26-31)? _____

5. What was Jesus to accomplish (Lke. 1:32-33)? _____
_____

A. Could Jesus be reigning on the throne of David on the earth (Jer. 22:30—{Jesus is a descendent of Jeconiah - Matt. 1:11})? _____
_____

6. Is there a difference in the "church" and the "kingdom" (Matt. 16:17-19)? _____
_____

7. What did Jesus understand His purpose to be (John 18:37)? _____
_____

Biblical Position - Kingdom/Church Established

8. Who had prophesied of the events of Acts 2, the establishment of the church (Acts 2:16)? _____

9. What connection did Peter make in Acts 2:30? _____
_____

10. Where is Jesus (Acts 2:33)? _____

    A. Who prophesied of Jesus' position as King (Acts 2:34-35)? _____
    _____

11. What is the "mystery" (Eph. 3:3-7)? _____

12. Clues were given in the Old Testament that the Gentiles would be part of the Messianic Kingdom. However, this "mystery" was not fully revealed until the New Testament.

    A. From what Old Testament prophet did James quote to prove the Gentiles are now part of God's people (Acts 15:14-17)? _____
    _____
    _____

    B. Was this a new part of the plan of God (Acts 15:18)? _____

    C. What Old Testament prophet prophesied of the Gentiles being a part of God's people (Rom. 9:24-26)? _____
    _____

12. How long was the church in the plan of God? Does it have a secondary importance (Eph. 3:10-11)? _____
_____

THE "RAPTURE"

Premillennial Position

Tim LaHaye and Jerry Jenkins wrote a series of novels describing the events of the last days, including the rapture. One book begins with Rayford Steele, the captain of a 747, en route over the Atlantic to London. He leaves the controls to his co-pilot to take a break. As he walks out of the cock pit, he is met by a terrified flight attendant Hattie Durham. "'People are missing' she manages to whisper, burying her head in his chest.' Rayford Steele looks for an explanation, Maybe they are in the lavatory, or it was too dark to see them or they were hiding? She says, 'Ray, their shoes, their socks, their clothes, everything was left behind. These people are gone!'" (Left Behind, p. 16) The world is thrown into chaos because, at the same moment, others have vanished: bus and car drivers, air traffic controllers, school teachers, policemen, secretaries, and all the children. Those left behind begin to search for clues to understand what happened to all these people. Meanwhile, a one world government is being set up, the anti-Christ is revealed, and the 7 years of tribulation begin.

Throughout the denominational world, the rapture is viewed as looming in the imminent future. One man told me, "Don't buy any green bananas."

In the book, 88 Reasons Why The Rapture Will Be In 1988, reason #44 has 13 parts. The first, "From 28 A.D., when Jesus revealed himself to the Apostles as the Son of God (John 5:10-38), we have 28 A.D. + (7 x 280) = 1988, the Rapture of the Church year. Seven means complete, and 280 means the gestation period (of a human child); therefore, the numbers would say that the complete gestation period of the Church has been accomplished, and the Church is now ready to be born into eternity in the House of God in heaven." (Whisenant, p.29)

"Some Bible teachers see the second coming in two phases. The Rapture of the church is the first phase and Christ's glorious coming in power to the earth is the second." (LaHaye, Charting the End Times, p. 111)

LaHaye mentions various views of when the rapture will take place.

1. Pre-Tribulation View—Jesus will rapture the church before the Seven Year Tribulation period. According to LaHaye, "This is the prevailing view" (Charting the End Times, p. 106).

2. Partial Rapture View—"Christ will only rapture those 'that look for Him' (Heb.9:28), causing some Christians to enter the Tribulation but be raptured at another time during that traumatic period in one of the subsequent raptures. This view is not popular today" (Charting the End Times, p. 106)

3. Mid-Tribulation View—"Christ raptures His church in the middle of the Tribulation" (Charting the End Times, p. 106)

4. The Post-Tribulation View—"This view is second in popularity after the pre-Trib position. Christ will come at the end of the Tribulation, which means the church will go through the Tribulation and be raptured just before the glorious appearing. Thus those who are raptured zip right up to the sky then right back down." (Charting the End Times, p.106-107)

Biblical Position - The Resurrection

1. Concerning what two groups of people did Paul give instruction (1 Thess.4:13-15)?
_____

 A. Why might the Christians have concern for their fellow-Christians who had died?
 _____
 _____

 B. Does this context discuss what will happen to the non-Christian? Why not? _____
 _____

2. What will be the sequence of events at the coming of the Lord (1 Thess.4:16-17)?
_____
_____

 A. In 1 Thess. 4:17, the term "caught up" is "rapiermur" in the Latin Vulgate. From this Latin term, we get our English term "rapture." Will Christians be "raptured" (1 Thess. 4:17)? _____
 _____

3. Concerning what two groups of people did Paul give instruction (1 Thess. 5:1-11)?
_____

4. Most Premillennialists believe 1 Thess. 4:13-17 refers to the rapture of the church BEFORE the Tribulation period and 1 Thess. 5:1-11 is referring to Jesus returning to earth AFTER the Tribulation period. Do the events of these verses take place in two different timeframes (like the Premillennialists believe) or do all these verses refer to events which will take place in the same timeframe? Please explain your answer. _____

_____

_____

5. What will happen to the non-Christians when "the Lord Jesus is revealed from Heaven" (2 Thess. 1:6-10)? _____

_____

6. What will happen to the Christians when "the Lord Jesus is revealed from Heaven" (2 Thess. 1:6-10)? _____

_____

A. Is this a description of two different days or the same day? _____

7. What will happen to "those who have done evil" when the "hour" comes (John 5:28-29)? _____

8. What will happen to "those who have done good" when the "hour" comes (John 5:28-29)? _____

A. Is this a description of two different days or the same day? _____

9. "When the Son of Man comes in His glory", what will happen to the "goats" (Matt. 25:31- 46, especially v. 46)? _____

_____

10. "When the Son of Man comes in His glory", what will happen to the "sheep" (Matt. 25:31-46, especially v. 46)? _____

_____

11. When men are raised, what kind of body will they have (1 Cor. 15:42-44)? _____

_____

12. If the Premillennialist is correct, Christians with resurrected/spiritual bodies will enter the kingdom of God on earth. Is this possible (1 Cor. 15:50)? _____

_____

THE "TRIBULATION" - MATTHEW 24

Premillennial Position

"The reason the Tribulation will be a holocaust of major proportions is because it combines the wrath of God, the fury of Satan, and the evil nature of man run wild. Take the horror of every war since time began, throw in every natural disaster in recorded history, and cast off all restraints so that the unspeakable cruelty and hatred and injustice of man toward his fellow men can fully mature, and compress all that into a period of seven years. Even if you could imagine such a horror, it wouldn't approach the mind-boggling terror and turmoil of the Tribulation." (LaHaye, Charting End Times, p.58)

"The nature of the tribulation. ...First, it is a unique period. ...Secondly, it is a period of judgment upon the nations. ...Thirdly, it will be a period of persecution of Israel. ...Fourthly, it will be a period of salvation." (Charles Ryrie, The Basis of the Premillennial Faith, p.141-142)

The Premillennialist believes Revelation 6-19 and Matthew 24 describe the Tribulation. See Hal Lindsay's chart from There's a New World Coming on page 6 of this workbook.

Concerning Matthew 24, LaHaye says, "The first thing our Lord wanted His disciples— and us—to know about the end times is that there will be many deceivers and false messiahs who lead people astray. . . . Historically the church age has seen many false religious teachers but they will be even more pronounced just before the Tribulation and increasingly throughout it." (Charting End Times, p.35)

"What are the signs of the end times? The first sign Jesus pointed to was war. Not just any war, of which the world has seen over 15,000 to date, but a special war started by two nations and joined by many other nations on either side until all the world is involved. It was to be the greatest war in human history. That occurred with World War I in 1914-1918. Since then there have been a parade of 'signs', the most significant one being the regathering of the Jewish people back into the land of Israel and the recognition of Israel as a nation in 1948. Many other signs have occurred in fulfillment of Matthew 24:8 . . . This is why we consider the signs of our times to be setting the stage for the Tribulation." (LaHaye p.35-36)

"Much confusion has resulted from many well-meaning people trying to identify the 'generation [that] will not pass away until all these take place' (Matthew 24:34). Some start this generation at verse 31 and believe that it's talking about the generation beginning at the time Israel became a nation in 1948. The passage of time, of course, has disproved that idea. [He is referring to the quote below by Hal Lindsay in 1970 JRA] It's better to interpret this verse in its context: that is, the generation that sees the events of the Tribulation will also see the coming of Christ and the other events leading to the end of the age. . . . As soon as Antichrist and Israel sign a peace treaty, which he breaks in the middle of the Tribulation, there will be seven years until the coming of Christ." (LaHaye p.37)

"'Truly I say to you, this generation will not pass away until all these things take place.' (Matt.24:34) What generation? Obviously, in context, the generation that would see the signs—chief among them the rebirth of Israel. A generation in the Bible is something like forty years. If this is a correct deduction, then within forty years or so of 1948, all these things could take place. Many scholars who have studied Bible prophecy all their lives believe that this is so." (Hal Lindsey, The Late Great Planet Earth, pp.42-54)

Biblical Position - Matthew 24 and the Destruction of Jerusalem

1. What prediction did Jesus make (Matt. 24:1-2)? _____
_____

2. What question(s) did the disciples ask Jesus about this prophecy (Matt. 24:3)? _____
_____

3. What time frame did Jesus place on the fulfillment of this prophecy (Matt. 24:34)?
_____

4. What was NOT a sign of the destruction (Matt. 24:4-6)? _____
_____

5. What was NOT a sign of the destruction (Matt. 24:7-8)? _____
_____

6. What would happen before the destruction (Matt. 24:9-13)? _____
_____

A. Was this fulfilled (Acts 8:1-2; 9:23, 29; 12:2; 13:45; 14:5, 19; 16:22-24; 17:5, 13; 19:29; 21:27; 1 Pet.4:12, etc.)? _____
_____

7. What would happen before the destruction (Matt. 24:14)? _____

_____

   A. When was this fulfilled (Col. 1:23)? _____

   _____

8. What was the sign that the end had come (Matt. 24:15)? _____

_____

   A. When was this fulfilled? _____

   _____

9. What was the person to do when he saw this sign (Matt. 24:16-20)? _____

_____

   A. Does this instruction make sense if Jesus was talking about the Tribulation period
     as the Premillennialist claims? _____

10. How terrible would this destruction be (Matt. 24:21-22)? _____

_____

   A. How many died in the destruction of Jerusalem? _____

11. The "coming of the Son of Man" was described in Matthew 24:27-31. Jesus used
    figurative language to describe God's coming in judgment against Jerusalem. This
    language was used in several other context in reference to God's judgment on a
    nation. Please read:

   A. Psalms 18:7-12 - when David was delivered from Saul.

   B. Isaiah 13:9-10 - prophecy of the destruction of Babylon.

   C. Isaiah 19:1 - prophecy of the destruction of Egypt.

   D. Jeremiah 4:27-29 - prophecy of the destruction of Judah by Babylon.

   E. Ezekiel 32:7-8 - prophecy of the destruction of Egypt.

   F. Micah 1:3-4 - prophecy of the destruction of Israel.

12. What was Jesus' admonition to His disciples (Matt.24:32-35)? _____

_____

APOCALYPTIC LITERATURE AND THE BATTLE OF ARMAGEDDON

Premillennial Position

The end of the Tribulation period is marked by the battle of Armageddon. "According to the Bible, great armies from the east and the west will gather and assemble on this plain. There will be threats to the power of the Antichrist from the south, and he will move to destroy a revived Babylon in the east before finally turning his forces toward Jerusalem to subdue and destroy it. As he and his armies approach Jerusalem, God will intervene and Jesus Chirst will return to rescue His people Israel. The Lord and His angelic army will destroy the armies, capture the Antichrist and the False Prophet, and cast them into the Lake of Fire." (LaHaye, Charting the End Times, p.63)

"It is logical to ask at this point, how is he going to make war with the saints when they are gone from the earth [because of the rapture 7 years earlier JRA]? 'The saints' are the people who are going to believe in Christ during this great period of conflict [Tribulation]. After the Christians are gone God is going to reveal Himself in a special way to 144,000 physical, literal Jews who are going to believe with a vengeance that Jesus is the Messiah. They are gong to be 144,000 Jewish Billy Grahams turned loose on this earth—the earth will never know a period of evangelism like this period. These Jewish people are going to make up for lost time. They are going to have the greatest number of converts in all history. . . However, the Antichrist is going to unleash a total persecution of these people. . . He will be the absolute dictator of the whole world!" (Lindsay, The Late Great Planet Earth, p.111)

Written in 1970, The Late Great Planet Earth further says, "Russia and her allies use this occasion to launch an invasion of the Middle East, which Russia has longed to do since the Napoleonic wars. ...The prophetic indication is that Israel will become one of the most prosperous nations on earth during the reign of the Antichrist. ...When the Russians invade the Middle East with amphibious and mechanized land forces, they will make a 'blitz-krieg' type of offensive through the area. ...The might of the Red Army is predicted. ...The United States may be aligned with the Western forces headed by the ten-nation Revived Roman Empire of Europe. ...As the incredible Oriental army of 200 million soldiers marches to the eastern banks of the Euphrates, the

Roman Dictator will begin to prepare his armies to meet them for the showdown in the Middle East. ...So here it is—the last great conflict. After the Antichrist assembles the forces of the rest of the whole world together, they meet the onrushing charge of the kings of the East in a battle line which will extend throughout Israel with the vortex centered at the Valley of Megiddo." (Lindsay, pp.154-165)

Biblical Position - Apocalyptic Language

1. Whose "revelation" is the book of Revelation (Rev. 1:1)? _____
_____

A. The word "revelation" is from the Greek word "apokalupsis." It means "an uncovering, a laying bare, making naked" (Thayer). With the use of symbols, images, and visions, Jesus uncovers and reveals a message to His servants of impending persecution and ultimate triumph. This highly symbolic writing has been termed "apocalyptic literature." The term "apocalyptic" comes from the word "apokalypsis." This literary style was used in times of intense trial and crisis. The Spirit chose this style in the book of Revelation to dramatize the conflict between Satan and Jesus which played out in the persecution of the Christians by Rome. Perhaps this symbolic language was used to protect the Christians. If these prophecies had been written in literal language, the Christians who held this book could have been charged with treason.

2. When John wrote this book in about 95 AD, when did he say the prophecies would come to pass (Rev. 1:1, 3; 22:6, 10)? _____
_____

3. To whom was the book addressed (Rev. 1:11)? _____
_____

4. What was the situation of the Christians at that time (Rev. 1:9; 2:2, 10, 13-14; 3:9)?
_____

5. Who was under the altar (Rev. 6:9)? _____

6. When did Jesus say the martyr's blood would be avenged (Rev. 6:10-11)? _____
_____

7. What was the word that reoccurs at the end of each letter to the seven churches (Rev. 2:11, 17, 26; 3:5, 12, 21)? _____
_____

Biblical Position - The Battle of Armageddon

"Armageddon" in Revelation 16:16 means "Mount Megiddo." Megiddo was a physical place in northern Israel. The Bible speaks of the valley of Megiddo (2 Chron. 35:22), but there is no literal Mount Megiddo. The valley of Megiddo was a place where decisive battles took place in Old Testament history, like "the Alamo" or "Pearl Harbor" in modern times. For example, Joshua defeated the king of Megiddo in Joshua 12:21; Deborah and Barak defeated Jabin and Sisera of the Canaanites in Judges 5:19; Saul and Jonathan died in battle at the eastern extremity of the plain in 1 Sam.31:1-6; Josiah died in a battle with Pharaoh Necho in 2 Kings 23:29-30.

8. When the sixth bowl of wrath is poured out, forces were gathered for a great battle. Who led the forces into this battle (Rev. 16:12-14, 16)? _____

_____

9. The battle does not take place until Revelation 19:11-21. Who wins the battle? _____

_____

10. The Premillennialist demands all prophecies be viewed literally, such as the "1,000 year reign." However, he is inconsistent when viewing aspects like the "frogs" and "dragon" symbolically. Are the following to be taken literally or symbolically?

A. the waters of the Euphrates "dried up" _____

B. "unclean spirits like frogs coming out of the mouth" _____

C. "the dragon" _____

D. "the beast" _____

E. gather "the whole earth" _____

F. place called "Armageddon" _____

11. What is the point of this symbolic battle? _____

THE MILLENNIAL REIGN

Premillennial Position

"The millennium is the period of a thousand years of the visible, earthly reign of the Lord Jesus Christ, who after His return from heaven, will fulfill during that period the promises contained in the Abrahamic, Davidic, and new covenants to Israel, will bring the whole world to a knowledge of God, and will lift the curse from the whole creation." (Ryrie, The Basis of the Premillennial Faith, p.145-146)

"Three groups of people will be related to the millennial government. Israel, regathered and turned to the Lord in salvation, will be exalted, blessed, and favored throughout the period. The nations will be subjects of the King during the millennium. In addition, the Church will reign with Christ, not a subject of the King, but as one who rightfully shares the rule. (Ryrie, pp.149-150)

"Christian ordinances will be terminated at the beginning of the millennium." (Ryrie, p.150)

"Therefore, the temple will be there, but will offerings be continued after Christ returns and is personally reigning? Premillennialists in general answer in the affirmative." (Ryrie, p.152)

"The Millennium will be a time in which the Adamic curse will be rolled back, except for death, and in which people will live for 1000 years. ...The Millennium will be a time of tremendous environmental transformation ... the desert will blossom . . will be abundant rainfall in areas that today are known for their dryness ... the predatory instincts of animals will cease. . physical conditions for people will also drastically change for the better ... many physical infirmities and health concerns will be eradicated ... absence of sickness and deformity ... will minimize the differences between those who still have mortal bodies and those who have resurrected bodies ... The Millennium will be an era of great spiritual awareness, sensitivity, and activity for both Christians and the restored nation of Israel ... Unfortunately in the midst of such pristine conditions, there will still be human rebellion. Because the complete effects of the Fall will not have been erased, there will be one final revolt against the righteous government of Jesus Christ. This will occur at the end of the Millennium." (LaHaye, Charting the End Times, pp.70-72)

"The sequence is clear in the last chapters of Revelation. First there is the return of Christ at the climax of the greatest war of all time. Second, Christ separates the surviving believers from the surviving unbelievers; the unbelievers will be judged and cast off the earth (Rev. 20:1-6; cf. Matthew 25:41-46). Third, Christ establishes the millennial kingdom and the surviving believers go into it as mortals and repopulate the earth (Rev.20:11-15; cf. Matthew 25:31-40). Fourth, at the end of a thousand years the unbelieving children rebel, Christ judges them, then He completely changes the old heaven and earth and creates a new one (Rev.21; Isaiah 65:17; 2 Peter 3:8-13). This is the ultimate destiny of all persons who are redeemed by Christ." Hal Lindsay, The Late Great Planet Earth, p.178)

Biblical Position - The 1,000 Year Reign

1. What was to happen to Satan during the 1,000 years (Rev. 20:1-3)? _____
_____

2. Who were sitting on the thrones (Rev. 20:4)? _____
_____

    A. Did these souls literally have no head? _____

    B. What is the point of the figure?_____
    _____

    C. Previously in the book, where had John seen these souls (Rev. 6:9) _____
    _____

    D. How long until they would be avenged (Rev. 6:10-11)? _____
    _____

3. How long would they live and reign with Christ (Rev. 20:4)? _____

    A. Is this "thousand years" literal or figurative? What is the point? _____
    _____

4. What was the value of this passage to persecuted first century Christians? _____
_____

5. Notice what is NOT in Revelation 20:

- the second coming of Christ
- the bodily resurrection
- Jesus coming back to the earth
- reign on earth (can disembodied souls reign on the earth?)
- David's throne
- the length of Jesus' reign
- Jerusalem of Palestine
- Us (those of us who still have our heads)

The Premillennialists look forward to the 1,000 year reign as the time of the greatest blessings on earth. The Bible teaches the spiritual blessings of Christ are the time of the greatest blessings on earth.

6. Where are all spiritual blessings found (Eph. 1:3)? _____
_____

7. Pick out some words and phrases used by Paul which indicate there is not going to be another time on the earth of greater blessings than what we have right now in Christ. Eph. 1:4-14 - _____
_____
_____
_____

8. In Isaiah 2:4, Isaiah prophesied of a time of great peace. What kind of peace do we have in Christ right now (Eph. 2:11-18; Gal. 3:26-29)? _____
_____

9. Can we be in Christ's kingdom today (Col. 1:13)? _____

10. In what position are Christians today (1 Pet. 2:5,9-10)? _____
_____

JUDGMENT DAY AND ETERNITY

Premillennial Position

In a discussion of 2 Peter 3:10-13, Lindsay said, "In other words, Christ is going 'to loose' the atoms of the galaxy in which we live. No wonder there will be a great roar and intense heat and fire. Then Christ will put the atoms back together to form a new heaven and earth, in which only glorified persons without their sinful natures will live. There will be no more rebellion of man's will against God; only righteousness, peace, security, harmony, and joy." (The Late Great Planet Earth, p.179)

"Three destructions of the earth are described in the Bible, one past and two yet to come. The first destruction came when the Flood covered the earth in the days of Noah, sparing only eight righteous persons. ...However, two more destructions are predicted in the Bible. One will come by fire, after which God will restore all things (2 Peter 3:4-14; see also Isaiah 65:17-20). ...since 2 Peter 3:10 refers to the Day of the Lord, we are inclined to believe that he meant the second catastrophic event that will come upon the earth, producing a refurbished earth to begin the millennium. The other destruction is described in Revelation 21:1. 'Then I saw a new heaven and a new earth; for the first heaven and the first earth passed away, and there is no longer any sea." After God does away with this planet as we know it, He will create a new heaven and a new earth. They will be better than anything this world has ever known, including the Garden of Eden. There will be changes ... For example, there will no longer be any seas. Two-thirds of the present earth's surface is covered by water; the remaining one-third includes many large areas rendered worthless because of mountains and deserts. Thus only a small portion of today's earth is inhabitable. ...God's Tabernacle will no longer be in the third heaven, for He will move His headquarters to the new earth and will literally take up His abode in the New Jerusalem ... The wiping away of all tears means that the normal reaction of sorrow will be eliminated ... This is an almost certain indication that God will create for us a dimension that we cannot yet comprehend. He is planning an entirely new way of life for His people." (LaHaye, Charting the End Times, p.75-77)

Biblical Position - Events of the Judgment Day

1. What will happen to the universe (2 Pet. 3:9-12)? _____
_____

2. Who will be raised from the dead (John 5:28-29)? _____
_____

3. Who will face Jesus the Judge (Matt. 25:31-46)? _____
_____

4. Where will Jesus be sitting (Rev. 20:11)? _____
_____

5. Who will be standing before Jesus (Rev. 20:12-13)? _____
_____

6. By what will they be judged (Rev. 20:12-13)? _____
_____

7. What is the destination of the lost and the saved (Rev. 20:14-15)? _____
_____

8. What will happen to the kingdom (1 Cor. 15:24)? _____
_____

Biblical Position - Eternity

9. What will replace the destroyed universe (2 Pet. 3:13; Rev. 21:1)? _____
_____

10. How is this place described (Rev. 21:2-8)? _____
_____

11. How is this place described (Rev. 21:9-21)? _____
_____

12. How is this place described (Rev. 21:22-22:5)? _____
_____
_____

CPSIA information can be obtained at www.ICGtesting.com
Printed in the USA
LVOW09s0417171115

462860LV00002B/2/P

Hawaii Goes to War

The Aftermath of Pearl Harbor

by

Wilbur D. Jones, Jr.
and Carroll Robbins Jones

WHITE MANE BOOKS
SHIPPENSBURG, PENNSYLVANIA

All photographs in this book were taken by Patricia O'Meara Robbins unless otherwise noted.

This White Mane Books publication
was printed by
Beidel Printing House, Inc.
63 West Burd Street
Shippensburg, PA 17257-0152 USA

The acid-free paper used in this book meets the guidelines for permanence and durability of the Committee on Production Guidelines for Book Longevity of the Council on Library Resources.

For a complete list of available publications
please write
White Mane Books
Division of White Mane Publishing Company, Inc.
P.O. Box 152
Shippensburg, PA 17257-0152 USA

Library of Congress Cataloging-in-Publication Data

Jones, Wilbur D.
      Hawaii goes to war : the aftermath of Pearl Harbor / by Wilbur D. Jones, Jr. and Carroll
Robbins Jones.
        p. cm.
      Includes bibliographical references and index.
      ISBN 1-57249-260-0 (alk. paper)
      1. Pearl Harbor (Hawaii), Attack on, 1941. 2. World War, 1939-1945--United
States--Hawaii. 3. World War, 1939-1945--Campaigns--Pacific Ocean. 4. Jones, Carroll
Robbins, 1934- 5. Robbins family. I. Jones, Carroll Robbins, 1934- II. Title.

D767.92 .J66 2001
940.54'26--dc21

                                                                                              2001023802

PRINTED IN THE UNITED STATES OF AMERICA